Who Stole the Tiger's Eye?

Story by Richard Gunther

THE CRIMES

Here are two cases for **you**, the ace detective of Ace Detective Agency, to solve: *Who Stole the Tiger's Eye* and *Find the Professor*.

Get a notepad and a good pen ready.

The cases aren't easy, and it will take all your powers of deduction to work out who the criminals are.

No looking at the clues at the back of the book! Good luck!

CASE NO. 1: WHO STOLE THE TIGER'S EYE?

The fabulous diamond known as the "Tiger's Eye," owned by the wealthy Mrs. Penelope Prigg, has been stolen. The crime occurred some time during the night, while Mrs. Prigg was asleep.

Mrs. Prigg is very upset, because the diamond was a gift to her from Sheik Ali Baba of Arabia. You have been called in to find the precious jewel. You must also discover who stole it.

Be careful—there are a few tricks thrown in to confuse you.

You drive to the huge mansion on Strawberry Hill and stop the car at the gates. You get out and have a careful look before driving up to the front door. Mrs. Prigg's room, where the Tiger's Eye was stolen, is second from the left upstairs.

The butler's room is second from the right on the ground floor. The maid's room is second from the left on the ground floor. In the distance, on the right, is an RV campsite, and on the left is a golf course.

You meet Mrs. Prigg and two of her three servants. Now you have four suspects:

1. Mrs. Prigg herself, who may have hidden the diamond so that she could claim the insurance.

2. Mr. Charles James Carryall, the butler, who may have wanted to give himself a huge bonus on top of his wages.

3. Ms. Andrea Philippa Dustoff, the maid, who might have slipped the precious jewel into her pocket while cleaning Mrs. Prigg's room.

4. The gardener, who is having the day off.

None of the suspects can really prove where he or she was when the Tiger's Eye was stolen.

Mrs. Prigg says:

"I am a heavy sleeper. If someone had come into my room during the night, I would not have heard them. I put the cat outside, then put the diamond in its case before I got into bed, and it was gone in the morning. That's all I know."

Mr. Carryall says:

"I sleep in a room on the ground floor, right next to the living room. I did not hear anything all night, except once, about midnight. There was a slight bumping sound, but I thought it was the cat."

Ms. Dustoff says:

"I went to the movies with the gardener and came home about midnight. The noise that Mr. Carryall heard was probably me in the kitchen. We don't have a cat. I was at the cupboard looking for some peanuts to nibble on."

Do you suspect any of these three? If so, which one, and why? Write your ideas down.

You go back to your office to think. This is going to be another tough case. There are no unusual fingerprints in Mrs. Prigg's room, and it is too far above the ground for a normal burglar to reach.

You wonder about the butler for a while, but there is one big problem with him: he has been a faithful worker for Mrs. Prigg for twelve years. It seems unlikely that he would ruin his career for the sake of some extra money.

The maid, Ms. Dustoff, has been with Mrs. Prigg for two years. She has no family except a brother somewhere, and Mrs. Prigg has been like a mother to her.

The gardener was not available for an interview. You call his number, but he is not home.

Just as you put the receiver down, the phone rings. On the other end is a voice. It sounds like the voice of a child. It speaks in a whisper.

"I cannot tell you my name. You must look for the diamond among the wanderers."

Click!

You scribble the message down and think about it for a while. What did the caller mean by "wanderers"?

You take down a dictionary from your bookshelf and flip through the pages.

wanderer—a tourist, excursionist, globe-trotter, explorer, adventurer, rover, straggler, rambler, vagrant, waif, stray, loafer, tramp, hobo, beachcomber, vagabond, nomad, sleepwalker, emigrant, fugitive, refugee.

Now you have some clues.

You underline the words that seem to be the most likely ones.

Now, using your computer, you check to see if there are any people in the district who match the words from the book.

There are no **globe-trotters**. You cross them off. There are no **explorers** or **adventurers**. Cross them off.

There are no people who visit beaches to scavenge for things, no **sleepwalkers**, and no **refugees**.

Gradually, by elimination, you get down to a short list.

You call the local hotel and find that they don't know of any **stragglers**, **ramblers**, **waifs**, **strays**, **loafers**, **tramps**, **nomads**, or **hobos**.

You call the police station and find that everything was quiet on the night of the crime. No trouble was reported from any **vagrants**, **rovers**, **vagabonds**, **fugitives**, or **emigrants**. The sergeant mentions an excursion bus, but it left with most of its passengers the day before. You cross off **excursionist** as well.

Suddenly, you have it! Of course. How could you have missed it? The word that catches the meaning of "wanderers" is staring right at you: Think about it. Go back to the house on page 5.

What do you see?

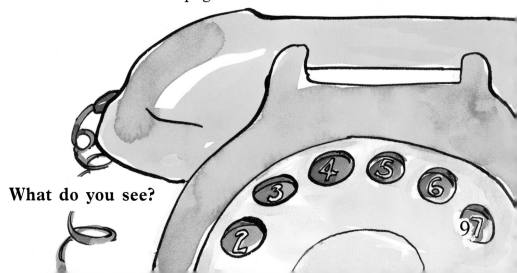

You visit the RV site and introduce yourself. All the campers are friendly—all, that is, except one. His name is Philippe Andreas.

"What are you doing here?" he demands.

"I'm looking for something," you reply.

"What?"

"Something valuable."

He looks interested. "Stolen, perhaps?" he says.

"Yes," you reply.

"Who from?"

"Mrs. Prigg," you say, watching his eyes for a reaction.

"Well, you won't find it here, so get out!" he says. "We don't like people coming around, poking their noses into our lives!"

You go, but not before you spot something interesting. Look at the picture carefully.

What seems to be strange? Write it down.

You head back to your car.

Suddenly: ZING! An arrow shoots past your ear and buries itself in a tree. A note is wrapped around it. You unroll the piece of paper and hurry back to your office, where you spread it out on your desk and study it.

The note is in some kind of code, and it is written in strange symbols.

Can you work it out?

Write down the answer on your detective pad.

You have cracked the code.

Now you have to find a map with the name "Bree" on it.

You wonder what the name "Bree" refers to. There seem to be four possibilities:

1. It might be a road.
2. It might be a landmark.
3. It might be a river.
4. It might be an ancient place name.

You find an old map and search for "Bree."

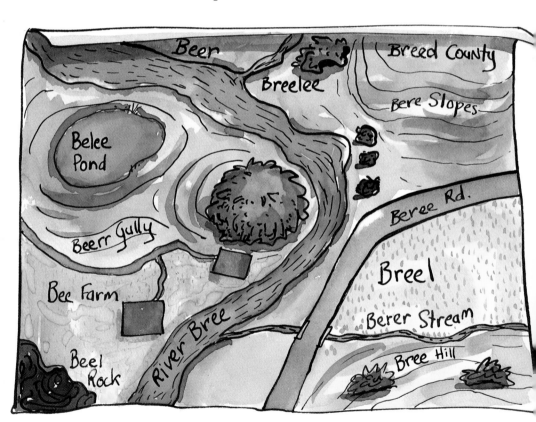

Write down what you think "Bree" could be.

Having found the "Bree," you drive to a place near it and walk across the fields until you come to some trees. As you approach, a man steps into view and stops you. It is Philippe.

"What are you doing here?" he snarls.

"I was just going to ask you the same question," you reply.

"You want the boy, don't you?" he says.

"Boy? What boy?" you ask.

"The rat who was going to meet you here," says Philippe. "He won't be coming now."

"What have you done to him?" you ask.

"None of your business," he snaps. "Now get out!"

"We'll meet again," you say, smiling.

You are pleased, because you have found a good reason to suspect this man, and you have also seen an important clue.

What clue did you see? Write it down on your detective pad.

Now that you have a good idea who committed the crime, you decide to track down the Tiger's Eye. You know that Philippe has something to do with the theft, so you wait until he goes and begin to follow him.

Being a trained detective, you have great powers of observation, so you have no trouble following Philippe's tracks through the grass. But when you come to a wide, sandy place, you almost lose the trail.

Then you remember something from page 14 and follow Philippe's tracks easily across to the other side of the sand.

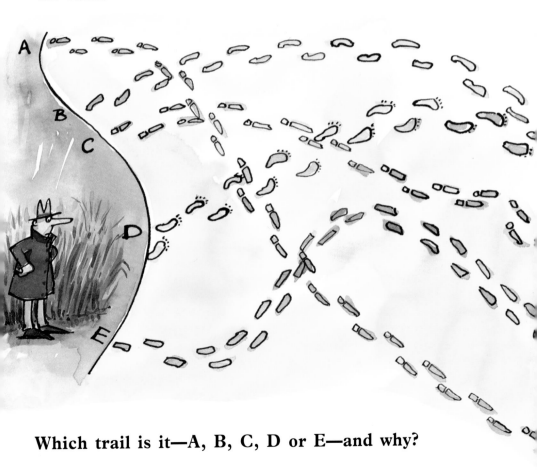

Which trail is it—A, B, C, D or E—and why?

Now you come to a shed surrounded by trees. You creep up to the side, where there is a small window, and look in. A boy is lying on the floor, hands bound and mouth gagged.

When the boy sees you, he stands up and comes over to the window. He cannot talk to you, but he uses his nose to write a message on the dusty glass.

The words are back to front, because the boy is on the opposite side of the window. You take out your detective pad and jot down the message. To read it correctly, you hold a mirror in front of it, so the message is the right way around.

What does it say?

Now you have to find a cup, held by something called a cupid. This has really stumped you, but you are a determined detective. You go for a stroll around the RV site, looking at the view, until you come to a statue.

What do you see? Is it a clue?

You realize that you have found the whereabouts of the diamond and also discovered the most likely suspect. Now all you have to do is wait, and the thief and his accomplice will arrive.

How do you know you have discovered the most likely suspect? (It has something to do with the statue.)

Sure enough, later that day, Philippe and his accomplice arrive. You arrest them both, and the diamond is returned to a very grateful Mrs. Prigg. Can you guess how the jewel was stolen? But there is a twist. Philippe has another accomplice.

Who do you think the accomplice is?

CASE NO. 2: FIND THE PROFESSOR

This case is even more difficult than the first one.

It involves the disappearance of Professor Frank Lee White.

Get out your detective notepad and pen, and get ready to solve the crime.

It is Monday morning. You have had a busy month solving crimes, but they have all been too easy. You want a challenge. You want something tough to try.

Your secretary brings you your morning mail. Apart from the usual bills and things, there is a crumpled old envelope. It looks as if it was dragged around in the dirt before it was sent to you.

You open the envelope and find a battered piece of paper with something scrawled across it. You cannot understand the words; they are in some kind of foreign language. But, thankfully, whoever sent the note has also given you some clue as to what the words say.

Some of the letters are given to you. All you have to do is match the letters with the same letters elsewhere in the message. (See page 22.)

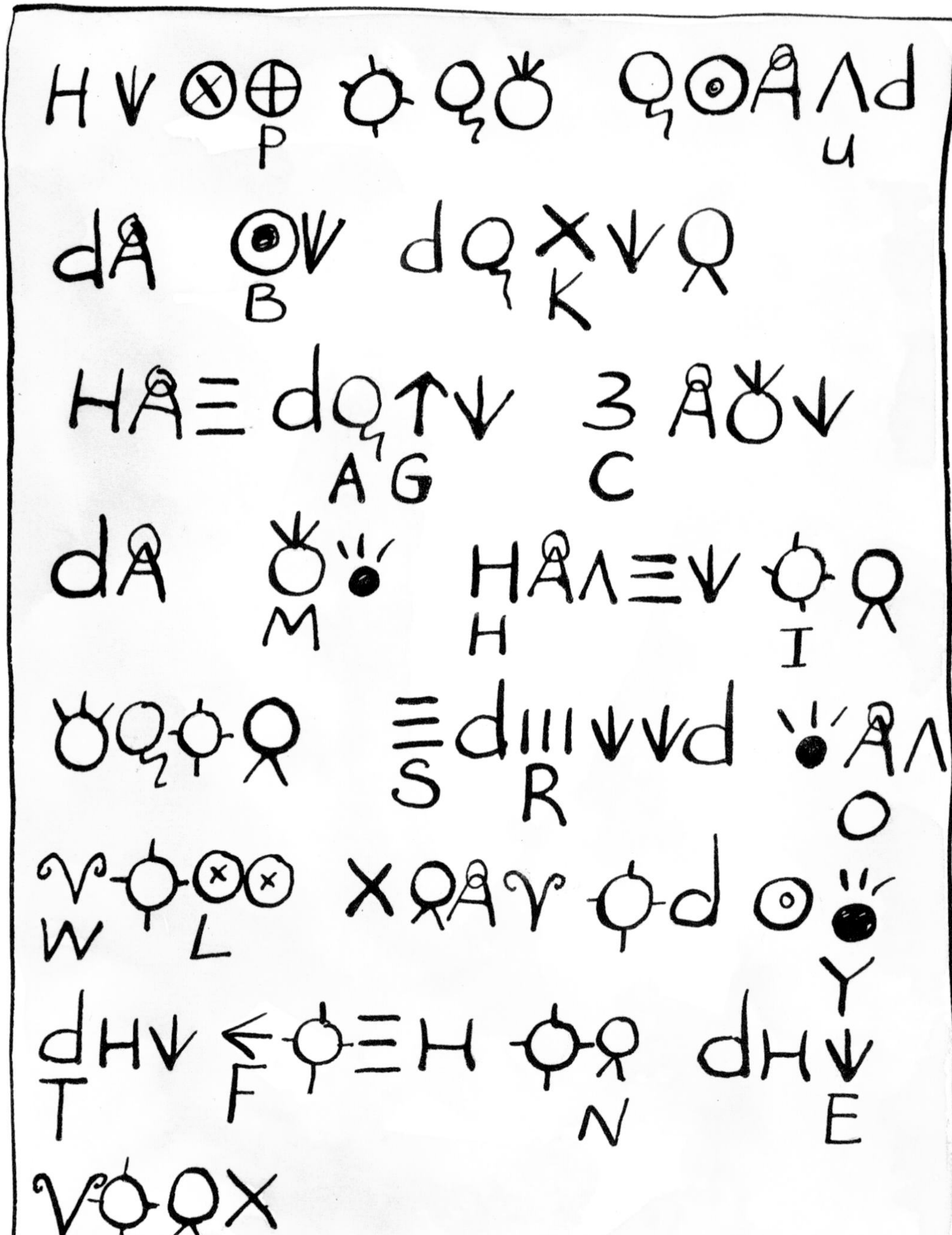
P
u
B
K
A G
C
M
H
I
S
R
O
W
L
Y
T
F
N
E
D

You search your excellent memory and realize that the professor who is missing is Frank Lee White, the famous dinosaur expert.

Now you need a map of the city to find the street the professor has named.

Time yourself to see how long it takes to discover where the street is on the map.

You drive to the street and look at the houses. One of these houses is the professor's, but which one? You look at the windows, the doors, the letterboxes, and the roofs. Suddenly you see what could be a clue.

The house number of the professor is easy to find, but be careful. There could be a red herring thrown in to trick you.

You go up to the back door and try it. It is unlocked. You go in. The place is a mess. Whoever took the professor had quite a struggle.

You look for clues.

"Aha!" you say, suddenly seeing a scrap of paper pinned to the wall. It has a symbol written on it. The professor has left something useful for you.

You find a book of scientific symbols in a bookcase and look for a match. At last you come to a list of elements.

List of Elements

V	: Vanadium	Hg	: Mercury
Cr	: Chromium	Ti	: Thallium
Mn	: Manganese	B	: Boron
Fe	: Iron	Bi	: Bismuth
Co	: Cobalt	Po	: Polonium
Ni	: Nickel	At	: Astatine
Cu	: Copper	Rn	: Radon
Zn	: Zinc	Fr	: Francium
Ga	: Gallium	Ra	: Radium
Ge	: Germanium	Bk	: Berkelium
As	: Arsenic	Ha	: Hahnium
Se	: Selenium	La	: Lanthanum
Br	: Bromine	Ce	: Cerium
Kr	: Krypton	Pr	: Praseodymium
Rb	: Rubidium	Nd	: Neodymium
Sr	: Strontium	Pm	: Promethium
Y	: Yttrium	Sm	: Samarium
Zr	: Zirconium	Eu	: Europium
Nb	: Niobium	Gd	: Gadolinium
Mo	: Molybdenum		

Now you have a name for the person who took the professor.

You decide to find out a bit more about this Berke fellow, so you go to the university where the professor was trained and ask to see a list of all the graduates who were at the university at the same time as the professor.

The university is only too happy to supply you with a list of names. You turn page after page until you come to:

Exceptional Graduates

E.B. Grewin	Q.L. Joker	G.M. Gregor
W.M. Line	O.W. Phar	C.R. Azee
R.A. Richards	N.M. Guffaw	P.N. Kings
S.T. Yawn	R.C. Gunther	U.P. Downside
D.M. Bruce	F.K. Inches	P.K. Ruthers
M.E. Tres	E.S. Phillips	M.I. Teemag
P.P. Pearson	U.G. First	P.R. Otector
I.M. Cleaner	S.L. Patrick	D.I. Erty
T.K. Barclay	N.S. Berke	S.A. Etyfirst
C.O. Ouper	C.C. Aiurns	B.A. Rrel
F.L. White	Q.U. Estions	C.R. Ombie
W.A. Tered	D.G. Udgison	D.R. Oughts
N.G. Tonny	F.U. Neesite	D.A. Tonne
N.O. Morlists		

Write down the two names you are looking for.

So now you know who took the professor.

You also know that the professor was taken in his own car, so you decide to check it out.

You go back to the professor's house and look for more clues. This time you try the garage and find the professor's vintage car.

You examine it, looking for tiny bits of evidence that might help you track down where the car has been recently.

Tiny fragments → of dry wood.

Fine, white, → sand grains.

Swamp grass → caught in the spokes.

Your conclusion is that the car has recently been to a place where there is sand, seaweed, and salt!

Now where could that be? (Write your answer down on your detective pad.)

30

But now you need to know which beach the professor's car has been to. The professor, as you know, lived on Main Street, so you drive your car from Main Street. But which way do you go?

Which roads lead to the beach? You try different routes but end up in dead ends.

Can you name the roads you take to get to the beach? Write down the roads and the name of the beach.

You drive to the beach and stop to admire the view. A fresh wind blows in your face, and the sun shines on the waves as they break along the **white sand**. Yes, this must be the place.

There are two clues why the professor must have been at this beach. One is easy—but what is the other one?

Get out your detective pad again!

Now you begin to look for something from the professor. If you are lucky, he might have dropped something to help you find him.

Sure enough, on the beach you find another scrap of paper, with a strange message on it.

You pull a dictionary out of your coat pocket and flip through the pages. In a few moments, you have worked out what the message means.

You quickly hire a boat and head across to the islands. As you expected, there is a cove in the second one, where a boat has already been pulled up. You notice right away that the professor is still able to walk.

How do you know?

You follow the tracks as far as the rocks, where they disappear. To carry on, you are forced to go along a narrow trench. This means that you are probably walking right into a trap, but you are a very brave detective, so you carry on regardless.

Soon you arrive at a signpost on the path. Berke has pinned a note there for you.

It reads:

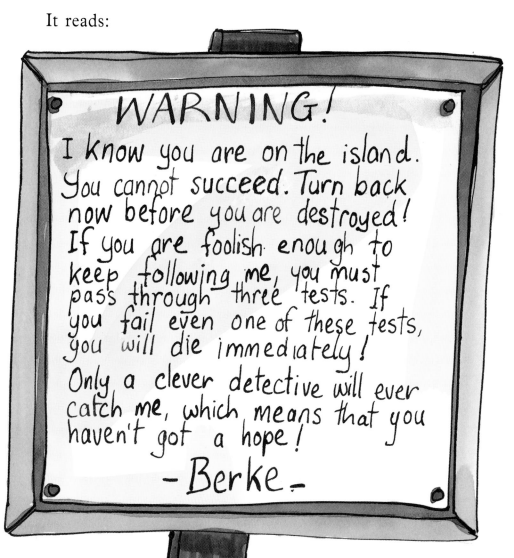

WARNING!
I know you are on the island.
You cannot succeed. Turn back
now before you are destroyed!
If you are foolish enough to
keep following me, you must
pass through three tests. If
you fail even one of these tests,
you will die immediately!
Only a clever detective will ever
catch me, which means that you
haven't got a hope!
— Berke —

You decide to keep following the path. It turns a corner and splits into two paths. A voice speaks to you from a speaker hidden in the rock:

"Welcome to the first test. Have you written your will? If you choose the wrong path, you will be blown to bits by dynamite. Here is the test. Imagine there are two people, one on the left path and one on the right. One of these people always tells the truth, but the other one always tells lies. You are permitted to ask only one question of each person. If you can detect the liar, take the path he is on."

After a moment's thought, you ask two questions, then choose the right-hand path, passing safely on. You walk along a groove in the rock until you come to a wall with a door, which completely blocks your path.

What did you ask?

You push the door and go in. You find yourself in a small room.

Suddenly, the door you came in slams shut behind you and locks itself.

You look around the small room and see no way to escape. Another door on the other side of the room is also locked.

The only object in the room is a large bathtub, with a faucet at one end. The faucet starts to shoot water into the bathtub until the bathtub is full and overflowing.

You watch as the water covers the floor and begins to rise. If you don't think of a way to stop the water, you will soon drown! You try the faucet, but it has no handle. You try bashing the door open, but it is too solid to move.

To save yourself from drowning, what do you do?
Write the answer down in your detective pad.

As soon as the waters begin to go down again, the door on the other side of the room opens, and you leave the room.

Now you have only one test left. You know Berke will be furious with you, so you expect something really difficult.

Sure enough, Berke is angry. "You'll never get out of this one!" he says through a speaker on the wall.

Suddenly, the ground falls away under you, and you drop into a deep hole. Luckily, the floor of the hole is made of soft soil. Halfway up the side of the hole is an opening, but it is too high to reach.

"If you don't think of a way out of there in twenty minutes," says Berke, "you will be blown sky-high!"

You look around. There are no tools in the hole. The walls are too slippery to climb. You cannot jump to the opening. It certainly looks hopeless this time! But you soon work it out and make it through the opening in less than ten minutes.

How did you do it?

40

You crawl along the narrow passage until you come to a high-tech laboratory.

Berke has his back to you. You drop down to the floor, and Berke turns to see what the noise is. The light flashes off his glasses as he gasps. He is very surprised to see you. He reaches for you, but you are faster.

"Hold it right there, Berke," you say.

He sneers at you, unafraid.

You whip around and grab the collar of another man, who is caught in the act of creeping up behind you.

What gave him away? How did you know he was creeping up behind you?

"Gave yourself away, didn't you," you say.

Berke scowls angrily.

"Hands up over your heads," you say. "Come on! Both of you!"

You take Berke and his sidekick, both safely handcuffed, back to the mainland and turn them over to the police.

Now, where is the professor? You must get through this maze in one minute to rescue him before a time bomb goes off. Ready, set, go!

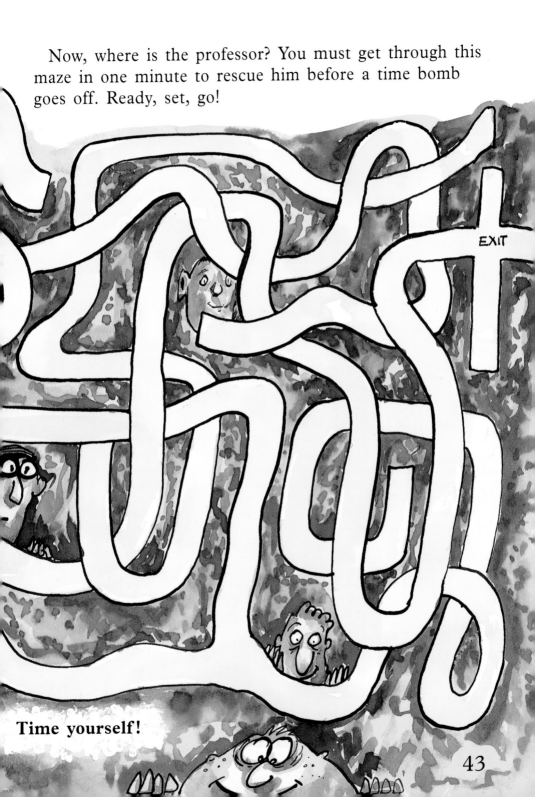

EXIT

Time yourself!

43

You get through just in time.

The professor is very pleased to be set free. He thanks you many times and gives you, as a show of his gratitude, one of his dinosaur bones.

Thank you.

The Clues

Congratulations! If you have gotten this far without looking, you have done very well. You have solved two major crimes. We will call on you again.

And now, for those junior detectives who may want to know how you solved this crime, here are the important clues your eagle eye spotted:

Pages 4–5
You have a keen eye. The room where Mrs. Prigg sleeps is high up. It would be difficult for a burglar to reach, unless the burglar climbed up the vines, but they would be too weak to support a human's weight. You notice the vines come from the second window on the ground floor, the maid's room. In the distance you notice some RVs, and you file this away in your mind for later reference.

Pages 6–7
You suspect Mrs. Prigg, because she may be bored with her wealthy lifestyle and want something exciting to happen. She might have hidden the diamond, either for the insurance or just for the fun of it.

You suspect Mr. Carryall, because he has access to Mrs. Prigg's rooms, he knows what is in them all, and he could easily have slipped the diamond into his pocket on his way through.

You suspect Ms. Dustoff, because she, like the butler, could easily have taken the diamond. However, she has a close relationship with Mrs. Prigg, and it seems doubtful that she would risk losing her job just for some quick money. But she was eating peanuts—and what likes peanuts?

Page 8
You hear a young voice. This means that a child is involved in the theft. The fact that this child is afraid to be identified means that he or she is close to the thief and perhaps even knows the thief quite well. This might suggest the thief is dangerous.

Page 9
The word left is "tourists," and there are always tourists at RV sites. You suspect the burglar may be a tourist.

Page 10

You noticed something on the roof of one of the RVs—a small monkey. Monkeys like peanuts. And who else likes peanuts? You also take note of the man's name. Where have you heard a similar name?

Page 11

The code has most of the letters but there are some that you have to guess at. You notice that nearly every word has an "ee" sound, so you fill in the missing letters and come up with: "MEET ME AT THE TREE AT THE BEND IN THE BREE AT THREE."

Page 12

The name of the river is the Bree. All you have to do is find the bend in it and hope you approach it from the correct side.

Page 14

You notice two things. One is the fact that Philippe is not wearing shoes, and the other thing is the monkey's tail, hanging from the branches. Now you may safely assume that Philippe has a pet monkey. You consider whether the monkey may be the one that climbed the vines of Mrs. Prigg's mansion and stole the diamond.

Page 15

Philippe really lets the cat out of the bag now. He admits he knows who your informant is, and he is dangerous, as you guessed he would be.

Philippe's tracks are easy to follow because, as you noticed, he has bare feet. There is only one trail of tracks with bare feet. That is track D.

Page 16

The message, when reversed by a mirror, reads: "T i in Cupid's cup." You realise that "T" stands for "Tiger," and "i" stands for "eye." Now all you have to do is find Cupid's cup. This makes you think of carvings, sculptures, statues . . . and you wonder if there might be a statue somewhere in the area.

Cupid is usually represented as a winged boy carrying a bow and arrow.

Page 17

You see a statue of Cupid.

Page 18

The most likely suspect? Easy. About the only thing that could climb up the Cupid statue is a monkey! This takes you back to Philippe, who could have made the monkey drop the diamond into the little cup on Cupid's head.

Page 19

The other accomplice in this crime is the maid. Her name is very much like Phillipe's name, but she sneakily turned hers around to confuse you! Philippe is really her brother. The vines in the picture went from the maid's window up to Mrs. Prigg's. The monkey climbed up after the maid's brother slipped it into his sister's room at midnight. Both the butler and Mrs. Prigg said there was a cat. The maid was lying. Did you work that out?

Here are the clues to Case No. 2, which your eagle eye spotted:

Page 22

The code reads: "HELP. I AM ABOUT TO BE TAKEN HOSTAGE. COME TO MY HOUSE ON MAIN STREET. YOU WILL KNOW IT BY THE FISH IN THE WIND. PROFESSOR."

Page 23

Main Street is near the bottom right-hand corner of the map.

Page 25

The "fish in the wind" is on the roof of number 11. It turns in the wind to show the direction the wind is blowing—just the sort of thing you'd expect a scientist to have.

Page 27

The symbol Bk matches Berkelium—Berke for short.

Page 28

The two names you want are F.L. White (the professor) and N.S. Berke.

Pages 30–31

The clues all relate to the beach.

Pages 32–33

The streets are Main Street, then along Sea Road, onto Dog Street, along Short Street and onto Stephens Road, then into Hill Crescent, and down to Sunny Beach.

Page 34
The two reasons are: 1. The beach is made of white sand, which matches the sand from the car. 2. There are oil drips on the parking spot.

Page 35
The strange message is easy to work out if you know what the words mean. *Bk* stands for Berke, *+* stands for *and*, *Candid* stands for *Frank* (as in Frank White, the professor), the arrow shows that the two named people have gone somewhere, *archipelago* means *islands*, and *to number 2* means they have gone to the second of the two islands. *Hurry* and the sun going down means "Please come before the sun sets."

Page 36
You see two sets of footprints, which means that the professor is able to walk.

Page 38
You asked both people a question to which you already knew the correct answer, such as "Is water wet?" The one who always lied would have to say "No."

Page 39
To save yourself from drowning, all you have to do is pull the plug out of the bathtub!

Page 40
You are down in the hole. You remember that the ground under you is soft soil. You can dig it with your hands. You dig all the soil from one side of the floor up into a pile against the other side of the hole, stand on top of it, and reach the opening.

Page 41
What gave Berke away was the reflection in his glasses. You saw a movement there. And you knew there had to be at least one other partner involved with Berke, because someone drove the professor's car back to its garage after he had been kidnapped.

Pages 42–43
The passage to take is B.

Well done—and we'll see you again the next time Ace Detective Agency needs a top detective!